Brian rides again!

Mr Keeping lives in Number 15, Wellington Square.
Mr Keeping lives with a snake called Bruce.
Mr Keeping was also looking after a chimp called Brian.

9

14

The Castle of Fun

Shall we go in the Castle of Fun?

We'll wait here.

Tessa and Brian went across the drawbridge into the Castle of Fun. In front of them were a very big girl and a very big chimp!

Brian put out his arm.
So did the big chimp!

Brian jumped up and down.
So did the big chimp!

Brian stopped.
So did the big chimp!

Brian pulled Tessa back over the drawbridge.
Brian was only a small chimp.
The chimp who lived in the castle
looked a lot bigger than him.

Brian thought the roundabout was fun.
He thought that riding the little bike was fun,
but he thought that riding in the dodgem car was
really great!

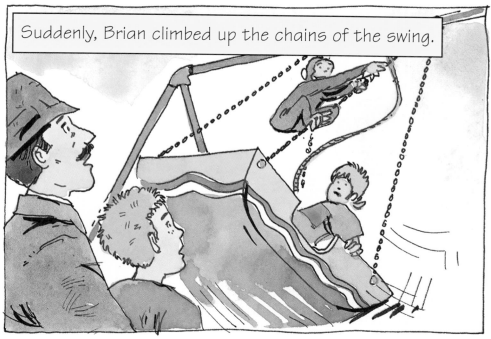

It was very dark in the tunnel.
There were spooky pictures of ghosts on the wall.
Brian heard the sounds of chains rattling.

Something flew over Brian.
It looked like a great big caterpillar.

Something was making strange noises. Was it an owl, or was it a ghost?

Something rattled in front of Brian.

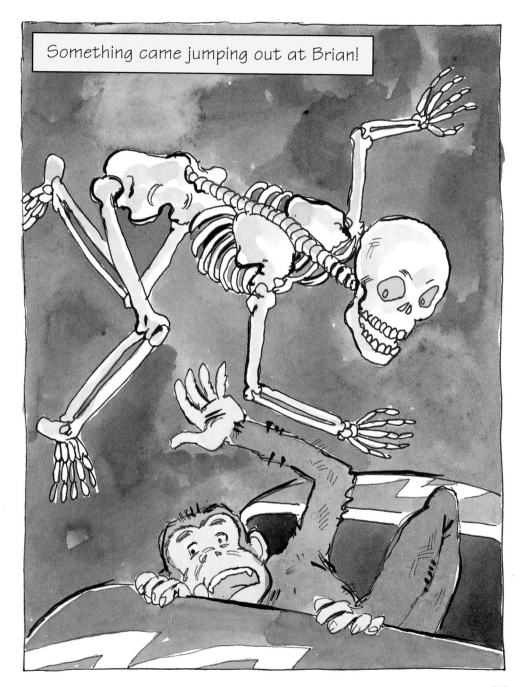

Something came jumping out at Brian!

The front of the ghost train was
built like the head of a dragon.
Brian looked as if he had just seen a dragon!

Look!
There he is, on the ghost train.

He looks really scared.
I think the ghosts have frightened him.

Come on, Brian.
Did the ghost train give you a fright?
It's time we were leaving.
It's time to go home.